EVERYO... GOIN... DAIRY-FREE!

33

34

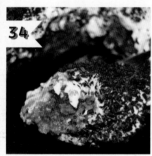

Compiled by: Jane Easton
Editor: Juliet Gellatley
Photos: Viva!
© Viva! 2016
Cover photo of Luxury Chocolate
Mousse p.33 by Chava Eichner/Viva!
ISBN: 978-0-9571874-1-2

Produced by: Viva!, 8 York Court,
Wilder St, Bristol BS2 8QH
0117 944 1000
(Mon-Fri 9am-6pm)

info@viva.org.uk
www.viva.org.uk
www.vivahealth.org.uk
www.whitelies.org.uk
www.veganrecipeclub.org.uk
www.viva.org.uk/30dayvegan
www.vivashop.org.uk
www.myvegantown.org.uk

CONTENTS

Viva! is Europe's largest vegan campaigning charity. We help people to reduce meat, fish and dairy in their diet and to go vegetarian and vegan. We are here to support them all the way! We campaign to end animal suffering and cruelty by showing the reality of modern farming and slaughter. Our undercover teams expose the conditions in factory farms and regularly grab the headlines.

Our major work on dairy is *White Lies*, which relies on years of research into the impact of dairy farming on animal welfare and our health. The campaign includes a film and report – *The Dark Side of Dairy* – which expose the conditions modern dairy cows have to endure and reveals the shocking fate of their calves. Our fully-referenced, scientific report, *White Lies*, looks at the impact of dairy consumption on our health and shows how dairy is linked to many degenerative diseases – from eczema and osteoporosis to breast cancer.

Viva! also produces books and guides on all the main veggie issues – and publishes the highly-acclaimed magazine, *Viva!Life*. Our Incredible Vegan Roadshows have been to more than 30 cities around the UK.

Viva!Health is part of Viva!. We educate the public on the value of vegan diets that promote good health and reduce the risk of disease.

We have a wide range of easy-to-read guides, including *Healthy Veggie (vegan) Kids*, *Vegetarian & Vegan Mother & Baby Guide*, the *D- Diet (Defeating Diabetes)*, the *Soya Story* (the truth about healthy soya) and the *5:2 Diet Vegan Style*. Our simple fact sheets focus on individual nutrients such as protein, calcium and iron.

Viva! Shop offers a superb range of high-quality merchandise and books by mail order. Goodies on offer include dairy-free chocolates, vegan wines, cruelty free gifts and clothing and vegan recipe books **www.vivashop.org.uk**

WELCOME

So you're thinking about going dairy-free. Well done! Not only will the decision make you feel better, look better and reduce your chances of several major diseases, it will also help to save animals from suffering and dramatically reduce your impact on the environment.

This booklet will guide you along the path to a dairy-free diet. We've mostly listed dairy replacements here but there is a vast range of other products suitable for vegans which are listed in the *L-Plate Vegan* guide. See page 7: *Useful Resources*.

WHY DAIRY-FREE

1 IT'S NATURAL TO BE DAIRY-FREE!

Most people in the world avoid milk and dairy products altogether because they are lactose intolerant – are unable to digest the sugar in milk (lactose). This is the percentage of peoples who are lactose intolerant:

95%	75%	50%	10%
Asian people	Afro-Caribbean people	Mediterranean people	Northern European people

(Source: NHS Direct)

All babies produce an enzyme called lactase, which is needed to digest lactose (milk sugar) but most lose it after weaning, at around the age of two. Without lactase, lactose ferments in the large intestine and produces gas. The result can be nausea, cramps, bloating, wind and diarrhoea, which usually appear a couple of hours after eating. The treatment is… avoid lactose by cutting out all dairy foods. You'll need to check labels on bread, chocolate and other processed foods where dairy products may be used.

There are around 5,000 species of mammal and none consumes dairy after weaning – apart from humans. We are also the only mammal to consume the milk of a different species. Imagine a squirrel raiding a sheep or goats' udder, or a bear cub feeding from an elephant – that gives you some idea of just how unnatural it is!

2 DAIRY-FREE IS GOOD FOR YOU

Despite industry hype that we need dairy for its calcium to build strong bones, the evidence points in the other direction. Westerners consume the most dairy yet have the highest levels of osteoporosis (brittle bones) in the world! (See our guide, *Building Bones for Life* at **www.vivahealth.org.uk**).

Ironically, in other parts of the world where people eat little or no dairy and obtain their calcium from plant sources, levels of osteoporosis are low. And there are plenty of healthier plant sources of calcium (see page 6): green leafy vegetables, sesame and other seeds, the whole range of pulses such as soya, peas, beans and lentils and the products made from them (tahini, hummus, tofu and the like), nuts and many fruits. There is a long, long list and the calcium obtained from them is easy for our bodies to absorb and store.

Dairy is also strongly associated with diseases such as breast and prostate cancers, diabetes, eczema and heart disease amongst others. For more information, see our *Why You Don't Need Dairy* guide and referenced *White Lies* report at **www.whitelies.org.uk.**

3 IT'S GETTING EASIER AND EASIER

There are now five million dairy-free consumers in the UK (Alpro, 2012) as well as millions of vegetarians, vegans and meat and dairy reducers. It is the perfect time to join them.

The free-from market includes dairy-free products and is one of the largest growth-sectors in the food industry. Every supermarket has free-from shelves.

Soya milk is now widely available from chain coffee stores.

There is a wide variety of dairy-free alternatives to cheese, milk, yoghurt and other dairy products.

Most chain restaurants and other eateries carry a free-from/allergen, vegetarian and vegan list of

CALCIUM-RICH FOODS

Almonds

Amaranth grain

Asparagus

Apricots (dried)

Artichokes

Baked beans (haricot)

Blackberries

Blackstrap molasses

Blackcurrants

Bok choy

Brazil nuts

Bread (wholemeal)

Broccoli

Chickpeas

Cinnamon

Edamame (soya beans)

Fennel

Kale

Kidney beans

Olives

Oranges

Sesame seeds
(and other seeds)

Soya milk (fortified)

Spring greens

Tofu

Swede

Walnuts

Watercress

6

dishes and must state which of their other dishes is suitable for such groups.

4 IT'S KINDER TO ANIMALS

The modern dairy industry is far from the buttercup-strewn meadow of advertising myth and is actually very brutal.

To produce milk, cows must repeatedly be made pregnant. Their babies are always taken away from them and if male, are killed shortly after birth or reared for veal or beef. Females are usually kept in solitary confinement for eight weeks before being used to replenish the herd.

Dairy cows are killed between five to six years old, the human equivalent of a twenty year old, because they are exhausted, infertile, diseased or their milk production has reduced.

Unbelievably, every year some 150,000 UK dairy cows are pregnant when they're killed, many in the final trimester of their nine-month pregnancy.

Goats also have to be made pregnant if they're to be milked. All kids are taken from their mothers immediately – the males killed for meat, often by religious slaughter methods.

A sheep's male babies are killed whilst still lambs and the females are mostly kept for breeding – slaughtered when they are too weak to bear more lambs or milk.

5 IT'S BETTER FOR THE ENVIRONMENT

The United Nations estimates that livestock for meat and dairy create 18 per cent of all greenhouse gases – that's more than all transportation put together, including air transport.

Worldwide, over 57 billion farmed animals are killed every year for meat.

Their digestion process produces huge amounts of methane while their manure produces nitrous oxide – both powerful greenhouse gases.

Livestock are the main cause of deforestation (United Nations) as trees are felled to provide grazing or to grow fodder crops. They are also the main cause of species (biodiversity) loss. Almost every environmental problem has livestock farming at its heart.

Farmed animals are extraordinarily wasteful as most of what they eat does not produce meat but simply keeps them alive and functioning. It can take as much as 17kg of vegetable protein to produce just 1kg of meat protein. Starvation across the world is intimately linked to farming livestock.

SUPERMARKET LISTS

- **ALDI** Google 'Aldi vegan list' for a full list
- **CO-OP** Vegan (and therefore dairy-free) items are clearly marked on their own-brand products where appropriate.
- **MARKS & SPENCER** health.marksandspencer.com Click on 'Help'. This takes you to an 'ask a question' box – enter 'vegetarian and vegan' to take you to vegan lists.
- **SAINSBURY'S** www.sainsburys-live-well-for-less.co.uk Enter 'vegan' in the search box. Many of their own-brand products are also labelled vegan.
- **TESCO** www.realfood.tesco.com Scroll to bottom of page, find the 'Healthy Eating' column then click on 'vegetarian and vegan'.
- **WAITROSE** www.waitrose.com Enter 'dietary and lifestyle' in search box then click on that link.

DAIRY-FREE OR ALLERGEN-FREE

If an item supposedly contains no dairy ingredients but the packaging states 'may contain traces of milk', it means the item is most likely dairy-free and vegan. However, it won't necessarily be suitable for those with an allergy to dairy.

Companies who make a variety of foods have to clean production line machinery between different batches that may contain nuts, soya, dairy, eggs and so on. A chocolate manufacturer may make a batch of milk chocolate, clean the line and then make a batch of dark chocolate that is dairy-free/vegan!

Although production lines are scrupulously cleaned, there is always the risk of microscopic food traces being left behind and companies have a legal obligation to warn allergy sufferers about possible cross contamination. From an ethical or health point of view, most vegan groups agree that this is an acceptable compromise and it widens the range of dairy-free/vegan products available – unless, of course, you are highly allergic to dairy. When in doubt, check with the manufacturer.

FFI see the Vegan Society's useful article **www.vegansociety/com/about/policies/allergy-labelling.aspx**

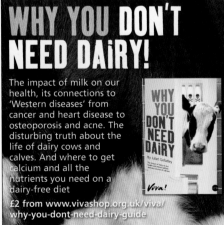

WHY YOU DON'T NEED DAiRY!

The impact of milk on our health, its connections to 'Western diseases' from cancer and heart disease to osteoporosis and acne. The disturbing truth about the life of dairy cows and calves. And where to get calcium and all the nutrients you need on a dairy-free diet

£2 from www.vivashop.org.uk/viva/why-you-dont-need-dairy-guide

WHERE TO SHOP

Unless an item is marked clearly as dairy-free or vegan, always read the label. When in doubt, ask an assistant or ask to see the shop's vegan list.

SUPERMARKETS

All major supermarkets sell an ever-increasing range of dairy-free and vegan products and many have their own free-from and vegan lists for own-brand products – see page 8. Aldi and Lidl sometimes label vegan products.

HOLLAND & BARRETT
They sell a large range of dairy-free/vegan products – how much depends on the branch.

INDEPENDENT HEALTH FOOD SHOPS They usually carry a good range of products and staff are more likely to be well informed.

ETHNIC FOOD STORES Chinese, Thai, Korean, Japanese etc usually carry a wonderful stock of dairy-free products – tofu, mock meats, spices and cooking sauces in particular are often excellent quality and value.

ONLINE STORES

Those listed below sell a wealth of vegan/dairy-free products and of course, they deliver! They often carry a bigger and better range than can be found in high street outlets. A web search will help you find more stores.

VIVA! SHOP www.vivashop.org.uk your first stop for vegan confectionery and gifts.

ALTERNATIVE STORES
www.alternativestores.com all vegan/dairy-free.

AMAZON UK www.amazon.co.uk click on 'grocery' then enter 'vegan' in search box.

ANANDA www.anandafoods.co.uk sells dairy-free Parmesan and hard to find vegan foods.

GOODNESS www.goodnessdirect.co.uk search 'vegan' for pages of food products. They also have a handy dietary key – dairy-free, vegan, gluten-free, organic etc.

HONEST TO GOODNESS www.honest-to-goodness.org.uk all vegan/dairy-free.

OCADO www.ocado.com – an online supermarket. Type 'vegan' in 'find a product'.

V-BITES www.vbites.eu/food mock meats, fish, cheese etc – all vegan/dairy-free.

VEGAN CO www.vegan.co.uk food, pet food, clothing, household and more – all vegan and dairy-free.

VEGAN STORE www.veganstore.co.uk clothing, footwear, food, cosmetics and toiletries – all vegan/dairy-free.

VEGAN X www.vegancross.com apparel, footwear, grocery (food, cosmetics, toiletries and more), books, accessories – all vegan/dairy-free.

VEGGIE STUFF www.veggiestuff.com food (including chocolate and sweets); pet food; body care and nutritional products – all vegan/dairy-free.

VEGUSTO www.vegusto.co.uk mock meats and cheeses, all vegan/dairy-free.

For more information see the *L-Plate Vegan* www.vivashop.org.uk/books/l-plate-vegan-guide.

1 NUTRITIONAL YEAST FLAKES

What is it? Sprinkles of naturally brewed yeast flakes in a tub (not to be confused with brewer's yeast!). It's full of protein, B vitamins and other useful nutrients – the blue tub in particular.

What does it taste like? Slightly cheezy, nutty, savoury. It dissolves into hot dishes really well or can be sprinkled on pasta, asparagus or soups for added taste.

What is it used for?
- pasta dishes and pasta sauces
- sprinkle on soups of most types
- bread – can be mixed with vegan spread to make garlic bread
- tofu scramble
- as a condiment or to make dairy-free cheezy sauces – see page 19-20

What brands should I look for? Engevita (Marigold).

Where can I buy it? Health food shops or online (see page 9). Not yet in supermarkets, other than online at Ocado, but we live in hope.

Can I make my own? No: it's a natural product but uses lots of beets and a fermentation process that would be difficult/impossible to recreate in a home kitchen.

2 SILKEN TOFU

What is it? A type of tofu (beancurd). All tofu is made from soya beans into a kind of cheese and is widely used throughout the Far East. There are lots of different types. Silken tofu is a softer, creamier variety – too squidgy for stir-fries but a very useful and versatile ingredient!

What does it taste like? It's bland but absorbs flavours very well. Creamy when whizzed up – but low fat and high in protein and calcium.

What is it used for?
- Sour cream alternative – see page 22
- Dairy/egg-free quiches
- Desserts such as cheesecake; chocolate mousse; raspberry mousse. See pages 33-36
- Search 'silken tofu' in **www.veganrecipeclub.org.uk** for a host of recipes

What brands should I look for?
- Longlife silken varieties (mostly 350g): Morinaga; Morinu; Blue Dragon; Clearspring
- Fresh silken: Taifun; Unicurd and generic silken tofu is sold in most Oriental stores

Where can I buy it? Large supermarkets, health food shops, Oriental food stores.

Can I make my own? Yes – it's not difficult! See **www.veganrecipeclub.org.uk** Home Made Tofu.

For further info on all types of tofu, see page 18.

3 AVOCADO

What is it? It's a fruit (not a vegetable) high in protein and healthy fats, amongst other things.

What does it taste like? Subtle – not sweet but creamy.

What is it used for?
- Desserts. Yes, really. Avocado lends itself to many dairy-free and vegan desserts and is especially good with chocolate, figs and pistachio nuts. Search the web for 'avocado vegan desserts' and you'll be amazed!
- Guacamole dip. See page 22
- Creamy pasta sauce. Mash or roughly chop avocado into cooked garlic and mushrooms then mix into spaghetti or linguini. Add lots of black pepper and a little salt

- Search for 'avocado' on www.veganrecipeclub.org.uk for the pasta recipe and a host of others

What brands should I look for? There are different types of avocado, eg Hass – small with lumpy dark green skins. Other types are larger and have smoother, paler green skins.

Where can I buy it? Ready-to-eat packs in supermarkets tend to be the most reliable but good greengrocers/vegetable shops may have ripened avocados going cheap. Make sure they are pretty soft and squidgy to the touch. If hard and unripe, you can keep them until they ripen.

Can I make my own? Sadly, avocados don't grow in the UK.

4 PURÉED WHITE BEANS

What is it? A creamy mixture made from white beans whizzed up – cannellini beans are best but haricot and butter beans will also work.

What does it taste like? It's all in the flavouring – adding fresh herbs, roast or fresh garlic, olive oil, black pepper and salt will transform these beans into a creamy delight.

What is it used for? Use to make recipes from www.veganrecipeclub.org.uk such as:
- Cannellini Bean, Black Olive, Sun-dried Tomato & Basil Pâté
- Artichoke, Butterbean & Filo Pie with Olives and Sundried Tomatoes (see page 28)
- Add a creamy but low-fat texture to soups, stews, sauces etc – just whizz up ¼-½ tin of white beans with a bit of the stock or juice from the dish you're making until smooth, then stir in

What brands should I look for? All white beans

are sold in tins. Sainsbury's Organic in cartons are a good deal.

Where can I buy it? Large supermarkets and health food shops – tins/cartons of cooked beans and packets of dried beans.

Can I make my own? Yes. Soak dried beans overnight. *If you are sensitive to beans, soak them for several days until they are almost sprouting. Keep in a cool place and change the water twice daily.* Rinse, drain and cook in fresh water – 40-60 minutes in an ordinary pan or pressure cook at high for 15 minutes. Blend beans wholly or partially to make the dish of your choice. Beans also freeze well, in bags or plastic containers.

5 NUT AND SEED BUTTERS

What is it? A rich butter/spread made from one or more nuts or seed – cashew, almond, Brazil, tahini (sesame seeds), sunflower, hemp, pumpkin – and the ubiquitous peanut. Sometimes ingredients are combined, such as almond, hazel & Brazil.

What does it taste like? Like the nut or seed it's made from and on whether they are raw or roasted.

What is it used for?
- Sauces such as tahini and miso, peanut satay, cheezy sauce (see page 19). Search 'sauces' on www.veganrecipeclub.org.uk
- Dips and spreads such as hummus (tahini – sesame paste)
- Adding to soups and stews for a rich, creamy texture and flavour – a tablespoon of peanut butter works wonders in Martin Shaw's Chilli non Carne www.veganrecipeclub.org.uk. A tablespoon of cashew or almond butter is delicious in tomato soup or sauce, to name just a few
- As a spread on toast etc – particularly nice with yeast extract (eg Marmite) or jam!

What brands should I look for? Biona, Carley's, Essential, Meridian, Monkey, Suma and Whole Earth are all good quality but there are lots out there.

Where can I buy it? Supermarket brands are cheaper but tend to be peanut based, padded out with other oils and contain too much sugar or salt. Wholefood and health shops tend to sell a larger variety of quality nut/seed butters but are usually more expensive.

Can I make my own? Yes – it's easy and tastes wonderful but you need a food processor with a good motor – Magimix or Vitamix. See **www.veganrecipeclub.org.uk** Home-made Nut & Seed Butter.

6 CHEEZY SAUCE MIX

What is it? Dairy-free cheese sauce mix in a tub – almost instant! Add it to plant milks such as soya, heat up and it's done.

What does it taste like? Pretty good! It's even better with a handful or two of nutritional yeast flakes and a teaspoon or two of Dijon mustard thrown in.

What is it used for? Any dish that needs a cheese sauce.
- Macaroni cheese
- Savoury pancakes
- Aurora sauce – mix half cheezy sauce with half tomato pasta sauce and add to tubular cooked pasta such as penne, rigatoni or macaroni

What brands should I look for? Free & Easy Dairy-Free Cheese Flavour Sauce Mix (black and yellow tub).

Where can I buy it? Health food shops, Holland & Barrett, Sainsbury's and online stores.

Can I make my own? Yes! See page 19-20 for recipes.

7 CREAM

What is it? Dairy-free cream.

What does it taste like? It depends on what it's made from. Commercial dairy-free creams are made from soya, oat, rice, coconut or nuts.

What is it used for?
- Add to a savoury creamy dish such as mushroom stroganoff or soup
- Desserts – single or whipping, depending on the pudding

What brands should I look for? Alpro/Provamel; Sojatoo; Oatly; Whiptop.

Where can I buy it? It depends on the brand and type of cream. All large supermarkets sell at least one type, eg soya (Alpro/Provamel) or oat (Oatly). For a wider range, try health food shops and online stores such as **www.vivashop.org.uk**.

Can I make my own? Cashew cream is very easy to make and is healthy, natural and delicious – use in savoury as well as sweet dishes. See page 21 for our recipe.

8 AQUAFABA

What is it? Tinned chickpea brine/goo (literally 'bean water') – the stuff we usually throw away. It's actually more of an egg replacer but too good not to share in this section!

What does it taste like? It is tasteless when mixed into other dishes.

What is it used for? 3 tbsp = 1 hen's egg. Its protein works like egg white so can be used to make meringues, cakes and much more.

What should I look for? Tinned chickpeas are best but aquafaba from tinned white beans (butter, cannellini, haricot) also works.

Where can I buy it? Anywhere that sells tinned beans! Value chickpeas work as well as organic and it doesn't matter if they're salted or not. It will keep for 3-4 days in the fridge in an air-tight container. Use the leftover chickpeas/beans to add to a curry, stew, make hummus or other dips…

Can I make my own? Possibly, in a pressure cooker, but the goo might not be as thick and protein-rich.

Recipes? Try 'Justine's Aquafaba Chocolate Mousse' on **www.veganrecipeclub.org.uk** For more, go to Facebook page 'Vegan Meringue – Hits and Misses!' for hundreds of tested recipes.

moo™ free

vegan chocolates

"**Taste like quality, milk chocolates, but made without any milk!**

OTHER DAIRY-FREE DELIGHTS

BUTTER AND SPREAD ALTERNATIVES

Most margarines/spreads are plant-based but manufacturers often add dairy, such as whey or butterfat. There are plenty that are vegan:

- **Biona**: all
- **Co-op**: Soft Spread
- **M&S**: Sunflower Spread; Sunflower Spread Light Dairy-Free
- **Pure**: Soya or Sunflower – widely available
- **Sainsbury**: Free From Spread
- **Suma**: Soya or Sunflower
- **Tesco**: Free From Soya Spread
- **Vitalite**

CHEESE ALTERNATIVES

Dairy-free cheese has improved over the years, as has the range of products and flavours available. There is no vegan Brie yet but who knows…?

Does it melt? Some dairy-free cheezes melt better than others.

What types are there?
Hard or creamy – with assorted flavours. See below.

- **Cheezly** (V-Bites brand).
  Hard cheese in around nine flavours including mozzarella, blue, cheddar and a rather good parmesan-style called 'Hard Italian-style'. Some flavours melt, others don't. Melting Cheezly, available in Mozzarella-style (good for pizzas). There is also a soya-free variety – and a Christmas selection pack. **www.vbites.eu/food**
- **Mozzarisella**. Melting mozzarella-style, made from rice milk – good on pizza or with tomato salad and the like. **www.mozzarisella.co.uk**
- **Sheese** Hard. 11 flavours such as Mild Cheddar Red Cheddar and including two melty flavours. creamy: five flavours ranging from Original (good for cheesecake) to Garlic & Herb. **www.buteisland.com**

- **Tesco**. Alternatives to hard and cream cheese sold in chilled, free-from sections in larger branches. Several flavours of each
- **Tofutti**. Creamy cheese: six flavours including Original (good for cheesecake); Garlic & Herb; Olive. All types are good on pizza
  Hard cheese: creamy smooth slices (Mozzarella and Cheddar); and grated Mozzarella – good for pizzas
- **Veganic**. So far mostly health food shops or online. Grated in a bag or sandwich slices
- **Vegusto No-Moo**. So far this Swiss company sells seven delicious flavours including Piquant (a bit like Parmesan); Walnut; Melty and more – also cheese sauce. They also sell deli slices, roasts and lots more. See page 9
- **Violife**: Pizza (block), assorted flavours in slices, Prosociano (parmesan style in a block)
- **Bellissimo Parmesan**. Vegan version from www.anandafoods.co.uk

CHOCOLATE

Dairy-free chocolate of all types is easy to find. Hooray! In supermarkets, most dairy-free milk chocolate is on free-from shelves but often, ordinary shelves contain products that are OK (eg Aldi mint thins). Get reading those labels or check out the supermarket vegan lists (see page 9.) Just remember to avoid things like butterfat, whey, cream, milk powder and other dairy items.

MILK CHOCOLATE

Dairy-free milk chocolate is made from plant milks – soya, rice or coconut.

Supermarkets: mainly on free-from shelves. Buttons and bars – also white buttons; Moo-free; Organica Couverture; Organica White; Plamil; Sainsbury's Crispy Rice Bar, Tesco Free-from chocolate bar.

Other brands: for some of the best vegan milk chocolate, check out **www.vivashop.org.uk** or try health food shops and online stores – see page 9. Our favourites include the divine Zotter Hazelnuss praline-style; hazelnut-studded Vego and Ombar Coconut Mylk raw chocolate.

PLAIN/DARK CHOCOLATE

There is plenty of high quality dark chocolate out there. Most is dairy-free but some have butterfat and other dairy bits so check the labels. Again, supermarkets carry a pretty good range but there's more choice in independent shops and online. Good brands include:

- **Aldi** – Moser Roth Dark 70%, Dark 85% and Dark Orange & Almond
- **Booja Booja** – the best truffles ever!
- **Kinnerton**
- **Lidl Fair Trade plain chocolate**
- **Montezuma**
- **Seed & Bean**

CREAM – see page 7

CUSTARD

Cartons, ready-made:
- **Alpro**
- **Provamel**

CUSTARD POWDER:

- **Birds** and most supermarket own-brands are suitable. Follow instructions on the tub but replace cow's milk with a plant milk. As fat levels of dairy milk are higher, you might want to reduce plant milk from 570ml to 450ml.

MILK ALTERNATIVES

There are far too many dairy-free milks to list – soya, rice, hemp, coconut, almond, oat, quinoa – with plain, strawberry or chocolate flavours. You'll find them in long-life cartons or fresh in chill cabinets of supermarkets and health food shops etc.

The taste varies – long-life is different from fresh; sweetened from unsweetened. It's worth experimenting. Many are fortified with vitamin B12 and calcium. Give it a couple of weeks and your tastes will change, to a point where dairy milks can quickly smell and taste very strange! See opposite for tips on using soya milk in coffee.

SOYA MILK

The most common brands are Alpro, Provamel (both non-GM) and So-Good – with every supermarket selling at least an own-brand long-life. Many also offer fresh soya milk. Most sell a value soya milk too. Plamil is also widely available – this all-vegan company made the first soya milk

in the UK and is the most ethically produced (*Ethical Consumer* magazine).

RICE MILK

Also easily found – Rice Dream is the most common brand.

COCONUT MILK

In a carton and made for pouring unlike the stuff in tins! There are many brands, including Kara and Tesco. They don't taste overly coconutty and are very nice.

NUT MILK

Hazelnut and almond are widely available – eg Ecomil and Tesco. Almond is gaining in popularity, with many prefering it in hot drinks.

HOME-MADE MILKS

Nut milks are simple to make. See our recipes for cashew milk and almond milk on page 23. Soya milk can be made at home with basic equipment or with a special soya milk maker. However, home-made milks are *not* fortified with calcium, B12 and other vitamins if that's what you want.

SOYA MILK IN HOT DRINKS

TEA: soya milk works well unless it's beginning to go off when it will curdle like dairy milk.

COFFEE: fresh soya milk doesn't usually curdle but long-life may. If using long-life in fresh coffee, heat the milk (don't boil) then add to the cup *before the coffee*. For instant coffee, add soya milk and hot water first, allowing the water to cool a little first. Add the granules *last* and stir vigorously.

NB Coffee houses such as Costa and Starbucks often use Alpro Pro soya milk, which never curdles and is delicious.

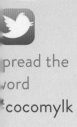

spread the
word
#cocomylk

Who needs dairy to make creamy, dreamy delicious chocolate?

Ombar Coco Mylk is a unique blend of organic raw cacao, coconut cream and vanilla. The only sugar we use is coconut sugar which adds a delicious caramel flavour. And just to be sure we've made chocolate that loves you back, we throw in a beneficial helping of biolive culture.

Available in great health food shops. If your local shop doesn't stock Ombar, ask them to feel the Ommm...

Plain and fruity varieties are available in several brands: Alpro, Co-Yo (coconut milk-based), Provamel, Tesco and our personal favourite, Sojade (health food shops, Ocado etc). Some live yoghurts are available.

Plain: use for savoury dips such as raita (see page 20) or use straight from the tub with curries, on cereal or where you would use dairy yoghurt.

Flavoured/fruity: eat as you would any other flavoured yoghurts.

Brands The brands above are the most common but the field is growing all the time. A fair-sized supermarket will sell at least one and a wider range can be found in health food shops or online.

Home-made is pretty easy to make but you'll need a small quantity of live vegan yoghurt as a starter culture. **www.veganrecipeclub.org.uk** and search 'yoghurt' for two recipes.

TOFU TYPES AND HOW TO USE THEM

What is it? Tofu or beancurd, is a kind of cheese made from soya beans. It's very high in protein and low in fat, making it a bit of a wonderfood.

Different types:

PLAIN
Cauldron; Dragonfly; Unicurd and lots of other brands are widely available, with Cauldron most readily available. Mainly used for stir-fries because it holds its shape but can also be deep-fried or oven-roasted.

STIR-FRIED TOFU
Drain the plain tofu and dry with kitchen paper. Chop into cubes or 'steaks.' In a frying pan or wok, heat 2-3 tbsp vegetable oil until very hot, add the tofu and fry for several minutes until golden brown. Turn gently while cooking to avoid mashing. Remove from pan and drizzle a little soya sauce over.

Options Crushed garlic, garlic paste, Chinese five spice powder or grated ginger (use your imagination) can be added a couple of minutes before the end of cooking. Can be pre-cooked and chilled until needed – 2-3 days in an airtight container lined with kitchen paper.

SMOKED TOFU
Taifun and other brands vary in texture and smokiness. Available in Waitrose, Ocado and health food shops. It can be cooked in the same way as plain, sliced thinly for sandwiches or fried up as rashers – again drizzled with soya sauce.

MARINATED TOFU
Cauldron marinated, ready-cooked pieces are available in health food shops and large supermarkets. Simple to use, they can be stirred into hot dishes at the end of cooking, particularly pastas, sauces, stews and stir fries. Also nice cold in salads.

SILKEN TOFU
Silken tofu has many uses – see pages 10, 20, 22, 29, 33-35.

For more information and recipes, see Viva!'s *The Soya Story* guide – free to download or cheap to buy: **www.vivahealth.org.uk/guides**

DAIRY-FREE!
RECIPES

It's never been easier to cook delicious vegan food. Below is a handful of useful recipes but do check out the amazing array of recipe books and websites on offer, including Viva!'s **www.veganrecipeclub.org.uk**. Also:

- The *Viva! Cookbook* – lots of quick and delicious meals
- The *L-Plate Vegan* – supermarket ready meal ideas
- *30 Day Vegan* – home-cooked and ready meal ideas

(See page 7 and 39 for details). You'll be spoiled for choice!

SAUCES, SIDES & MILKS

A TRIO OF CHEEZY SAUCES

1 CHEATIN'
SERVES: 2-4 | TIME; 5 MINUTES

- 3-4 tbsp Free & Easy Cheese Flavoured Sauce Mix (see page 12)
- 300ml unsweetened plant milk (soya, coconut, hemp, rice etc)
- ¼-½ cup nutritional yeast flakes (see page 10)

Optional: 1-2 tsp Dijon mustard

1 Whisk everything together in a small saucepan.
2 Bring to the boil gently, stirring continuously to avoid lumps (use a small balloon whisk and beat vigorously if lumps do form).
3 The sauce will thicken.
4 Serve while hot.

2 TAHINI OR CASHEW BASED
SERVES: 2-4 | TIME: 5 MINUTES

Version 1
- 200ml/7fl oz water
- 6 tbsp tahini OR 4 tbsp cashew butter
- 4 tbsp nutritional yeast flakes (see page 10)
- 1 tbsp fresh lemon juice
- 2 tbsp finely chopped shallot or red onion
- 2 tbsp light miso

1 Red onion and shallots are quite mild but if you find raw onion overpowering, cook it in a little oil or oil spray for a couple of minutes to soften first. Combine all ingredients and blend until smooth – if you have a hand/stick blender, this can all be done in the saucepan.
2 Heat gently without boiling before pouring over your meal – nut and seed butters become very thick if boiled.

Version 2 – Reduced Fat
As Version 1, but reduce tahini/cashew butter to 2 tbsp and add 60g/2oz plain tofu.

Version 3
As Version 1 or 2 but add a good pinch or more of smoked paprika, to taste.

3 TOFU BASED
SERVES: 4-6 | TIME: 15-20 MINUTES

- 1 shallot OR ¼ small red onion, finely chopped
- 1 medium clove garlic, crushed
- 2 squirts oil spray or a little plain oil
- 225/8oz plain tofu, any type (silken or firm)
- 500-600ml/18-21fl oz soya milk – start with less, add more if too thick
- Generous ½ cup/30g/1oz nutritional yeast flakes (see page 10)
- 2 tbsp cornflour OR 1 tbsp arrowroot
- 1 tbsp lemon juice
- 1 tbsp cider vinegar
- 2 tsp Dijon mustard
- ½-1 tsp salt, according to taste
- ½ tsp paprika
- ¼ tsp turmeric
- Generous pinch of mild chilli powder
- Black pepper

Optional: 1 tbsp pale miso

1 Measure all the dry ingredients and place in a container. Measure liquids and set aside. In a pan, sauté the onion and garlic in the oil spray until the onion is softened. If using onion and garlic powder, skip this step and go to Stage 2.

2 Meanwhile, blend the tofu until it is completely smooth – use a spatula to scrape down the sides of the bowl or food processor and integrate any lumpy bits.

3 Add the cooked onion/garlic plus the rest of the ingredients and blend again until it is smooth. Heat gently before using – bring to boil just enough to let the cornflour/arrowroot thicken the sauce.

RAITA: CUCUMBER YOGHURT DIP
SERVES: 2-4 | TIME: 5 MINUTES

- ¼ cucumber
- 250ml (half a large tub) of plain soya yoghurt – see page 18
- ½ tsp ground cumin
- Salt

1 Grate the cucumber then mix it in a bowl with the cumin and yoghurt. Mix the first three ingredients together in a bowl.

2 Taste, then add salt as desired. Will keep 2-3 days in a sealed container in the fridge.

Photo©Lisa @ www.storyofakitchen.com

CASHEW CREAM
SERVES: MAKES 2¼ CUPS THICK CREAM; 3½ THINNER CREAM | TIME: 10 MINUTES + OVERNIGHT SOAK

Basic Cream
- 2 cups whole raw (ie not roasted cashews). Don't use cashew pieces. They are cheaper but often rather dry and don't make such a rich cream
- Lots of cold water
- Flavourings – see ideas in the box or invent your own, according to the type of dish you want to make

1 Soak the nuts in cold water overnight first. Cover and refrigerate.
2 Drain the nuts and rinse in cold water. Place in food processor and do the following:
Thick cream: reduce the water – just cover the cashews with water in the food processor.
Thin cream: cover in water by over an inch/scant 2cm.
3 Blend at high speed for several minutes, until as smooth and creamy as possible. Sieve if still a bit grainy.

- The thick cream is vastly more adaptable so if you're going to freeze some, make it all thick – you can always thin down part of a batch
- The better your food processor, the better the creaminess. If you don't have a high-powered machine like a Vitamix or Magimix, there are several options
  - Grind the drained, soaked nuts first in an electric grinder (only takes a few seconds) then whizz them in the processor
  - If the cream is still a bit coarse, put through a fine mesh sieve. Ignore the grinder bit and just whizz up for as long as you can, scraping down the sides occasionally then sieve if still coarse
- Serving suggestions – just a few but get creative!
  - savoury – ravioli; lasagne; soups; dips and sauces. Adding lemon or chillies or smoked paprika or fresh herbs or garlic makes the cream even more adaptable in different dishes. We're sure you can come up with more ideas!
  - sweet – use as you would dairy cream. Adding sugar or agave syrup or vanilla or cinnamon or other lovely ingredients will allow you to get creative with desserts too
- Freezing: 3-6 months. It will need a whizz in the food processor to get rid of lumps before using

SOUR CREAM
SERVES: MAKES APPROXIMATELY 350G | TIME: 5 MINUTES

Tofutti make a great sour cream called 'Sour Supreme' but we have only found it online to date. But it's cheap, easy and very quick to make yourself!

This works very well with fajitas, chilli or mushroom stroganoff – or indeed, anything that requires sour cream in its recipe or as an accompaniment.

It will keep in an air-tight container for several days – or if you won't get through it, halve the recipe or else divide it into two containers and freeze one of them. When defrosted, give it a quick whizz with a hand blender or food processor before using.

- 1 pack firm silken tofu (approximately 350g) – Mori-nu or Blue Dragon brands available in large supermarkets such as Sainsbury and Waitrose
- 2 tbsp lemon juice
- 1 tbsp plain vegetable oil (not olive) – rapeseed oil (canola) is best because it is bland tasting. Use 2-3 tbsp more oil for a thicker cream with peaks
- 1 tsp cider vinegar
- 1 tsp sugar or agave syrup
- ½ tsp salt or a little more, according to taste

1 Blend the tofu until it is completely smooth and creamy and has lost its grainy texture.
2 Add the remaining ingredients and blend again until everything is well mixed in – if using extra oil, drizzle in slowly and blend in gradually. Taste and adjust seasoning/flavouring if necessary.

GUACAMOLE – AVOCADO DIP
SERVES: 2 | TIME: 5 MINUTES

- 1 large or 2 small ripe avocados
- Juice of ½ a lime or more to taste
- ½-1 large clove garlic, crushed
- Salt to taste
Options:
- 1-2 finely chopped tomatoes
- Handful of finely chopped coriander
- ½ red chilli, de-seeded and finely chopped – or a dash of hot pepper sauce eg Tabasco

1 Chop the avocado in half, remove the stone and remove the skin. Reserve the stone.
2 In a bowl, mash the flesh with a fork or potato masher then add everything else and mix in well. If making in advance, place in an airtight container with the stone – remove it before serving. (This helps to prevent the guacamole changing colour!)
3 Add a little garlic and lime juice and salt – too much garlic can kill the taste of the avocado, so adjust carefully.

EASY CASHEW MILK

SERVES: MAKES APPROXIMATELY 350ML/12FL OZ |TIME: 5-1O MINUTES PLUS 1 HOUR SOAKING TIME

This is particularly good if you want to make small quantities – nut milks are usually sold in 1L packs, which can be too large, especially if you live on your own. If you can buy loose nuts from a wholefood shop it will work out cheaper too. Just remember to buy 'raw' nuts – not roasted or salted.

Finally, don't throw the nut pulp away – add it to soups, stews or smoothies!

- ½ cup raw cashews (ie not roasted/salted)
- Square of clean muslin or cheesecloth approximately 40cm square
- Water to soak cashews
- 1½ cups cups water (350ml)
- Pinch of sea salt
- Agave syrup or concentrated apple juice to sweeten – whisk in 1 tsp, taste and add more if necessary

1 Cover the cashews in cold water, cover and allow them to soak for at least one hour. Drain and rinse.
2 Place the soaked cashews and the 1½ cups water into the blender or food processor. Whizz until smooth, at least one full minute. Add the sea salt and agave. Whizz again, taste and add a little more agave if necessary. If you prefer a less creamy milk, add a little more water – up to about ¼ cup/4 tbsp and whizz again.
3 Place the square of muslin over a sieve or colander which is placed over a bowl. Pour the nut mixture into the muslin then bring
the ends
together,
twist and
squeeze the
bag so that
the milk drips
into the bowl.
Twist more so
you get as
much of the
liquid out of
the bag.

4 Store the milk in an air-tight container. Store the nut pulp in another air-tight container and use within 3 days – add it to smoothies, soups or stews – anything you wish to thicken.

EASY ALMOND MILK

The technique, time, quantities and equipment are similar to the cashew milk recipe above. However, almonds come in different forms so there are different options.

- Use unskinned whole almonds and peel off the skins after soaking
- Use unskinned whole almonds but leave on the skins – they stay in the muslin bag anyway
- Use ready-skinned whole almonds. However, they are more expensive and commercial heat treatments to remove the skins mean a reduction in nutrients. You choose! Whatever you do, find a source of fresh, good quality raw (unroasted and unsalted) nuts
- 1 cup raw almonds
- Water for soaking nuts
- 2½-3 cups water
- 2 dates OR 1 tbsp agave syrup (optional)
- ½-1tsp vanilla essence (optional)
- Pinch salt

1 Soak the almonds in water overnight or for at least 6 hours.
Drain the
water from
the nuts and
discard it. If
removing
skins from
almonds,
do so now.

2 Blend
the nuts
with 2½
cups water and
other ingredients if using. Whizz until well-blended and almost smooth. Place a sieve or colander over a bowl and line it with a square of muslin or cheesecloth. Pour the mixture into the muslin, twist the material up and squeeze the milk through.
3 Taste the milk and add more water etc if desired. Place the milk in an airtight container and store in the fridge. It will keep up to 4 days. The pulp will also keep for up to 4 days if refrigerated and can be added to soups, smoothies or sauces.

CREAMY SCRAMBLED TOFU
SERVES: 2 | TIME: 10-15 MINUTES
One of our favourite light meals/snacks.

- 1 tbsp olive oil
- ½ onion
- 1 garlic clove, crushed
- 1 tbsp white flour
- ½ cup soya milk (120ml)
- 1 block plain firm tofu (200-250g) crumbled – not silken
- ½ tsp dried mixed herbs
- ½-2 tsp turmeric
- 1-2 medium vine tomatoes, finely chopped
- 2 tsp Dijon mustard
- Salt and lots of freshly ground black pepper
- 6 basil leaves chopped with scissors
- Bread for toasting

Optional: 2 handfuls of spinach leaves (add at stage 3 below); toasted seeds; brown sauce; soya sauce

1 Fry the onion and garlic on a low heat until soft.
2 Stir in the flour, followed by the soya milk. Stir in well to get rid of lumps and cook in for a minute or two.
3 Add the tofu, tomatoes, herbs, turmeric and mustard and stir for 5 minutes.
4 Make the toast and spread with margarine if desired. Spoon the scramble on the top, topped with the fresh chopped basil leaves. Some people like it as it is with lots of pepper, others like to add some/all the options!

BABY BROAD BEAN, TOMATO & FRESH HERB SALAD WITH CREAMY DRESSING

SERVES: 4-6 | TIME: 10 MINS

This is a very fresh, quick, simple salad. It is quite cheap, as well as being a good source of protein. It can be made into a more substantial meal with crusty bread or a simple wholegrain dish. Roasted vegetables would also go nicely.

Frozen broad beans aren't expensive. Alternatively, try delicious fresh soya beans (edamame), also frozen.

- 450g/1lb broad beans (frozen or fresh) or edamame
- 225g/8oz tomatoes – any sort
- Small bunch of rocket, washed and spun dry
- 1-2 tbsp chopped fresh herbs – eg fresh tarragon, flat-leafed parsley or coriander

Creamy Dressing
- 3 tbsp plain vegan yoghurt, such as Alpro, Tesco or Sojade
- 2 tbsp unsweetened dairy-free milk, eg soya, rice, coconut, oat
- 1-2 tsp Dijon or wholegrain mustard, to taste

1 Lightly steam the broad beans or edamame for a few minutes until tender – or if very fresh, use raw. If using tinned flageolet beans, just drain and rinse.
2 Chop the tomatoes into small pieces.
3 Chop the rocket with scissors.
4 Mix all ingredients together in a serving dish.
5 Make dressing by thoroughly mixing all three ingredients in a small bowl.
6 Pour dressing over salad, coating everything well and serve immediately.

SPEEDY PIZZA
SERVES: 2-4 | TIME: 25 MINS
Delicious vegan pizza. Use a vegan base (milk-free) such as
- JusRol Thin & Crispy Pizza Bases
- Napolina
- M&S pizza base
- Sainsbury's Thin & Crispy Twin Pizza Base OR Italian Pizza Base
- Waitrose Stoneground

Most packet mixes are vegan too. Spread with pizza topping plus thinly sliced veggies and vegan cheese of your choice (see page 15).

- 1 pizza base – ready-made or made from a mix
- Pizza topping from a jar. Alternatively, use a tomato-based pasta sauce or just some tomato purée
- 3 medium mushrooms, sliced thinly
- ½ small red pepper, cut into thin rings or slices
- Other veg of your choice: sweetcorn, olives, tinned artichoke hearts cut in half, thinly-sliced onions etc are all very good
- Olive oil
- A few handfuls of grated melting vegan cheese – see page 15
- Freshly ground black pepper

1 Preheat oven to temperature according to instructions on pizza base packet.
2 Spread pizza base with topping, then arrange vegetables and cheese artistically on top.
3 Bake for 10-15 minutes or until vegetables are just tender and the cheese has melted a bit.

ARTICHOKE, BUTTERBEAN & FILO PIE WITH OLIVES AND SUNDRIED TOMATOES

SERVES: 4-6 | TIME: 50-60 MINUTES – INCLUDES 20-30 MINUTES BAKING TIME

A deliciously creamy yet textured and tangy pie. Any type of artichoke hearts/bottoms can be used: oil-based ones are nicest but more expensive and higher in fat. And try experimenting with other ingredients – eg roasted red pepper in strips; grated vegan cheese grated on the top; leftover roast vegetables… you can even switch from white beans to others but the flavour will change too!

- 1 medium red onion, chopped plus a little olive oil or oil spray to cook
- 2 tins of butterbeans, rinsed and drained OR 480g home-cooked beans
- 2 tbsp finely chopped parsley plus more to taste if needed
- 2 tbsp olive oil (or soya milk if making reduced-fat version)
- 4 tsp lemon juice
- ½-1 tsp salt, according to taste
- Black pepper – freshly ground, to taste
- ⅛-¼ tsp cayenne pepper – start with minimum, taste and add more if desired
- 400g artichoke hearts or bottoms, drained – the chargrilled variety will add a different taste so you decide!
- 4 tbsp chopped pitted kalamata or black olives
- 3 large sundried tomatoes, chopped very small with scissors. Any type: in oil; dried that are rehydrated in hot water or slow roasted
- Filo pastry sheets (about ⅓ of a pack)
- Oil or oil spray to coat the filo layers – use olive oil or the flavoured oil from either a jar of artichoke hearts or sundried tomatoes. Use oil spray if you are watching your fat intake

1 Preheat the oven to 200°C/400°F/Gas Mark 6.

2 In a frying pan, wok or heavy-bottomed pan, heat a little olive oil/oil spray and sauté the onion until tender – add a little water if it starts to dry out.

3 Part-blend some of the butterbeans until smooth and creamy. Mash the rest gently with a potato masher – aim for some texture amongst the creamed beans. Add the olive oil, lemon juice, parsley, salt and cayenne. Mix in well.

4 Add the chopped artichoke hearts, olives and sundried tomatoes. Mix in gently. Taste the mixture and add more lemon juice/salt/pepper if necessary.

5 Oil a 20cm/8 inch square baking dish or tin- metal or ceramic. Remove the filo pastry from its packaging, open it out gently to lie flat and cover with a well-wrung out damp tea towel. This stops the pastry drying out and crumbling too much while you make the pie. Take one sheet off at a time and replace the tea towel.

6 Line the dish with several overlapping layers of filo sheets, oiling each layer well. You can use oil spray to reduce the fat content! Make sure the sheets overhang the tray so they can be folded back on top of the bake.

7 Spoon half the filling smoothly and evenly on top of the filo base. Fold over some of the filo layers, add more oiled filo and repeat with the second part of the filling. Finish the process with more layers of oiled filo.

8 Bake for 20-30 minutes or until golden brown. Remove from the oven. Allow to cool a little before slicing into portions.

LOW-FAT AND DIABETIC NOTES

The pie can be made using only oil spray so it is reduced fat but not super-low! However, a small portion would be fine. In addition…

- use low-fat sundried tomatoes (eg the slow roasted variety or ordinary dried ones that need to be pre-soaked in hot water)
- use tinned artichokes
- use soya milk instead of olive oil to mash and cream-up the beans
- don't add too many olives.

CREAMY VEGETABLE QUICHE

SERVES: 4-6 | TIME: 40 MINUTES

This is a great recipe and easily adapted – try other vegetables such as peppers or mushrooms.

- 1 block or sheet of ready-made pastry, eg Jus-Rol; Sainsbury's; Tesco

Filling
- 2 tsp olive oil
- 1 onion, roughly chopped
- 1 pack firm silken tofu, approximately 350g
- 1 tub (approximately 225g/8oz) savoury vegan cream cheese, eg Sheese Chives; Tesco Garlic & Herb Spread; Tofutti Garlic & Herbs
- 110ml/4fl oz soya or other unsweetened plant milk
- 1 tbsp Dijon mustard
- Salt and black pepper
- 1 head of broccoli, broken into florets
- 1 large red onion, chopped
- 6 medium tomatoes, sliced
- 100g (approximately ½ block) vegan cheese, grated, preferably a melting type. See page 15

1 Preheat oven to 190°C/375°F/Gas Mark 5. Blind bake the pastry:
- Lightly oil a quiche tin or dish (25-28 cm/10-11 inch).
- Roll out the pastry if in a block. Make the circle round enough so it fits the dish and overlaps 1-2cm above the edges (it shrinks when baked).
- Prick a few holes in the base with a fork and cover all the pastry with a sheet of greaseproof paper weighed down with a handful of dried beans.
- Cook for about 10 minutes then take it out of the oven.
- Remove the paper and beans and let it cool while you prepare the filling.

2 Meanwhile, make the filling:
- Sauté the onion 2 tsp oil until softened – about 3-5 minutes.
- Steam the broccoli florets for around 5 minutes and drain. Set aside.
- Blend the cream cheese, tofu, soya milk, Dijon mustard, salt and pepper until fairly smooth.

3 Arrange the onion, broccoli and tomato slices around the pastry case, evenly.

4 Pour the filling mixture on top, distributing it evenly with a spatula. Sprinkle the vegan cheese on the top.

5 Bake in the oven for 30-45 minutes or until firm in the middle. Check after 35 minutes, as the time will vary depending on your oven.

6 Allow to cool a little before cutting and serving.

MUSHROOM STROGANOFF

SERVES 4-6 | TIME: 40-50 MINUTES, INCLUDING PREPARATION

- 1½ heaped tbsp vegan margarine
- 2 tbsp olive oil
- 1 medium red onion, chopped quite thinly
- 2 cloves garlic, crushed
- 1.6K/3½lbs mushrooms, quartered – use a variety if you can get them. Chestnut or chestnut mixed with white are good
- ½ tsp paprika
- 150ml/5fl oz white wine
- 1 level tbsp cornflour
- 1 tub dairy-free cream, eg Alpro or Oatly
- 1 tbsp lemon juice
- Salt and lots of freshly ground black pepper
- Boiled rice or egg-free noodles to accompany

1 In a large saucepan or wok, heat the oil then melt the margarine in with it.

2 Lightly fry the onions and garlic until softened.

3 Add the mushrooms and simmer for 20-30 minutes or until the liquid has evaporated. Stir in the paprika and cook in for about a minute.

4 Put rice or noodles on now.

5 Meanwhile, add the wine to the stroganoff and cook in for about 5 minutes.

6 Mix the cornflour/arrowroot with a little water to make a paste. Add that to the stroganoff, stirring continuously until it thickens.

7 Add the dairy-free cream just before the end but don't boil.

8 Add the lemon juice and seasoning – taste and add more pepper etc if necessary.

9 Serve hot on a bed of rice or noodles.

Value mushrooms – a more economical way to make this dish!

QUICK MEXICAN MELLOW BLACK BEAN & COURGETTE CHILLI WITH ALL THE TRIMMINGS

SERVES: 4 | TIME: 25-30 MINUTES

This is kind of a cheatin' chilli! The main dish is easy to make plus the quick and simple sides make it a real feast – see the end of the recipe. If you're in a particular hurry or are slow at vegetable prep, buy ready-chopped, eg a mix of onions, courgette, peppers

- 1 tsp olive oil or use a couple of squirts of oil spray
- ¼ red onion or 1 large shallot, chopped quite small
- 2 cloves of garlic, crushed
- 2 courgettes, diced quite small – use peppers if not available or too expensive
- ½ green chilli, seeds removed and chopped very small (omit if using Discovery sauce, as below)
- ¼ tsp salt
- ⅓ cup black olives, chopped (a medium handful). You can buy ready chopped olives too!
- ½-1 tsp cumin powder (omit if using Discovery sauce as below)
- ½ tsp coriander powder (omit if using Discovery sauce as below)

- 1 jar of Discovery Fajita Season & Sauce (or other Mexican tomato-based sauce). Discovery brand is dairy-free, vegan, widely available and very good. It also comes with a spice pack on the top so you can omit the fresh chilli and spices listed above!
- 1 tin of black beans, rinsed and drained. Use kidney or pinto beans if you can't find black
- Corn tortillas or wheat-based wraps of your choice. Discovery, Old El Paso and many other brands are d-f/vegan, including Lidl

Options
- Rice or quinoa –from scratch OR from a pouch. Heat up according to the packet instructions. Brands include Uncle Ben, Tilda, Sainsbury's and Merchant Gourmet and include nutty, healthy brown rice
- Tomato salsa – bought or home-made
- Guacamole – see page 22
- Sour cream – see page 22 for our simple recipe
- Fresh coriander, finely chopped

1 Make the sour cream and guacamole now if using. Set aside.

2 Heat the oil/oil spray in a medium-large saucepan then add the red onion. Gently fry until softened then add the courgette and salt. Cook for several minutes, until the courgette starts to brown.

3 Add the garlic, olives and spices and cook for a couple of minutes more.

4 Add the fajita sauce and black beans. Cook for about 5 minutes until the sauce has absorbed all the flavours.

5 Meanwhile, warm the tortillas or wraps – microwave for 15 seconds then test and warm through more if necessary – just make sure they don't go hard. Alternatively, wrap in foil and warm in a medium oven for about 10 minutes. Heat the rice/quinoa now if using.

6 Serve the chilli with the wraps and the accompaniments on the side.

CREAMY LEEK & MUSHROOM PASTA
SERVES: 4 | TIME: 20 MINUTES

A fast and easy but delicious supper. It's very nice with one of our options below – plus steamed greens or a big salad.

- 60ml/4tbsp olive oil
- 3 leeks, sliced into rounds
- 2 garlic cloves, chopped
- 225g/8oz/3 cups chestnut mushrooms, sliced quite thickly
- 5ml/1tsp dried oregano
- 2.5ml/½tsp chilli flakes
- 375g/13oz/3 cups pasta of choice – noodles or spirali are good. Use rice or other g/f pasta/noodles for a gluten-free option
- 75ml/5tbsp vegan cream cheese, eg Sheese, Tesco or Tofutti – use plain or flavoured, according to personal taste. Eg chive and herb or garlic would work well
- 30ml/2tbsp chopped fresh parsley, to garnish
- Salt and freshly ground black pepper

Options
- Add creamed white beans – page 11
- Fry meat-free chicken pieces such as Fry's, V-Bites or Asda's in a separate pan and add to the pasta sauce just before serving
- Add marinated tofu pieces just before serving – see page 18

1 Heat water for pasta in a large pan.
2 Add pasta and cook 8-12 minutes, according to packet instructions and how soft you like to eat it.
3 Meanwhile, heat oil in a large heavy-based frying pan and sauté leeks and garlic for 3 minutes until soft.
4 Add mushrooms, oregano and chilli flakes and cook gently for 5 minutes more until mushrooms tender.
5 Drain pasta, reserving 60ml/4tbsp cooking water for mushroom mixture.
6 Stir this water into mixture, then add cream cheese and seasoning.
7 Heat gently for 1-2 minutes, stirring occasionally.
8 To serve, spoon sauce over the pasta and sprinkle with parsley.

DESSERTS

LUXURY CHOCOLATE MOUSSE

**SERVES: SERVES 6+ |
TIME: 25 MINUTES, PLUS
CHILLING TIME**

- 1 pack firm silken tofu (approximately 350g) available in good supermarkets or health stores. See page 10
- 150g dairy-free/vegan chocolate: use all dark OR 75g each of vegan 'milk' * and dark chocolate
- 3-4 tbsp maple or agave syrup (agave is available in large supermarkets. It's a bit like vegan honey) OR just use a bit of fine brown sugar
- ½ tsp vanilla extract
- Pinch salt

* Vegan milk chocolate: Moo-free; Organica; Plamil; supermarket free-from dairy-free 'milk' versions. See pages 15-16

Serving suggestions
- Dairy-free vegan cream (see page 12)
- Fruit coulis/sauce, eg blended blueberries or raspberries lightly sweetened
- Dairy-free vanilla ice cream eg Bessant & Drury; Booja Booja; Food Heaven; Razzle Dazzle; Swedish Glace; Toffuti – available from large supermarkets, Ocado or health food shops

Photo©Chava Eichner/Viva!

1 Blend tofu and salt until completely smooth and creamy, scraping the sides of the bowl to ensure everything is blended properly.
2 Melt the chocolate in a double boiler. That means that you heat a couple of inches of water to boiling point in a saucepan. Turn the heat down and place a heat-proof bowl over the pan of water, making sure that the bottom of the bowl doesn't touch the base of the pan. Now break the chocolate into chunks and place it in the bowl with the syrup and vanilla extract.

3 Stir gently with a rubber or plastic spatula until the chocolate has completely melted.
4 Add the chocolate mixture plus syrup/sugar to the tofu and blend again, using the spatula to scrape down the sides of the bowl, as before. Taste and add more sweetener if necessary and blend again.
5 Refrigerate in individual serving dishes of your choice for an hour or so – little expresso cups look lovely, or nice glasses.

TIRAMISU
SERVES: 6-8 | TIME: 30 MINUTES PLUS 1 HOUR CHILLING TIME

Base
- 4 thick slices of bread taken from a good quality large unsliced white loaf, preferably 1-2 days old. The bread needs to be fairly solid, not too fluffy. Slices need to be just under 2cm/1 inch
- 85ml/3fl oz soya milk
- ½ tsp vanilla extract
- 60g/2oz caster sugar
- 2 tbsp brandy or Amaretto liqueur (optional but very nice!)
- 2 tsp cocoa powder – not drinking chocolate

Mocha Crème Topping
- 110g/4oz unsalted cashew pieces (blanched almonds also work) – ground to a fine powder OR 5 tbsp cashew butter from a jar
- 1 pack firm silken tofu (approximately 350g), drained and pressed down to get rid of excess water
- 110g/4oz caster sugar
- 3 tsp instant coffee dissolved in a little just-boiled hot water to make a smooth syrup
- 1 tsp vanilla essence
- 1 tbsp cocoa powder – see above

Optional
- 50g (half a large bar) dark vegan chocolate – grated. See pages 15-16

1 Heat the soya milk and the caster sugar in a small saucepan until the sugar has dissolved. Add half teaspoon of vanilla essence plus the brandy/Amaretto if using, mix in well then turn off the heat.

2 Remove the crusts from the bread and discard. Cut each slice into four triangles. Arrange these on the bottom of a square lasagne type dish with as few gaps as possible. Pour the milk mixture over the bread evenly, sprinkle with the cocoa powder and set aside.

3 Grind the cashews to a fine powder if you haven't already done so. Set aside. Make the coffee mixture by pouring the hot water and coffee granules in the same saucepan and set aside.

4 Blend the drained silken tofu until very smooth and creamy then add the ground cashews. Use the spatula to mix in from the sides of the bowl every few seconds so there are no lumps. Add the sugar, vanilla extract and coffee mixture and blend again thoroughly.

5 Spoon the mixture evenly over the bread base then sprinkle the rest of the cocoa powder over evenly. Chill for at least an hour then top with grated chocolate if using before serving.

FRUITY CHEESECAKE

SERVES 6-8 | TIME: 30-40 MINUTES PLUS CHILLING TIME

This is delicious and easy to make. It is a great recipe that is easily adapted.

Mango cheesecake: use 1-2 ripe mangos, sliced, top with pecans and drizzle maple or agave syrup drizzled over everything
Chocolate cheesecake: stir in about 100-150g melted dairy-free chocolate to the tofu mixture

- 200g/7oz vegan biscuits, such as Dove's Farm Digestives; plain Hobnobs or McVitie's LIGHT Digestives (not the regular type)
- 75g/3oz vegan margarine, eg Pure
- 50ml/2fl oz soya or other plant milk
- 350g silken tofu, firm or soft – see page 10
- 200g/7oz plain (original) vegan cream cheese – eg Sheese, Tesco or Tofutti
- 1 tbsp vegetable oil
- 1-2 tbsp golden syrup
- 1 tsp vanilla essence
- ½ tsp lemon or orange essence (optional)
- 4 tsp cornflour OR 2 tsp arrowroot
- 150g/5oz fruit topping (eg fresh or defrosted frozen raspberries or strawberries) – sweeten with a little caster sugar or agave syrup if too tart

1 Preheat the oven to 350°F/180°C/Gas Mark 4.
2 Grind the biscuits (which will be used as the base for the cheesecake) until there are no large lumps left.
3 Melt the margarine and mix in the biscuit crumbs.
4 Spread in a greased flat tin – about 18cm/7inches diameter if round – or a 20cm/8 inch square will do also. A loose-bottomed springform is the easiest to use! Bake the base in the oven for 5 minutes.
5 Blend all the other ingredients thoroughly until smooth (except the fruit).
6 Remove the crumb mixture from the oven and pour the filling over the base.
7 Bake in the oven at the same temperature for 20 minutes, or until firm. Remove and leave to cool.
8 Top with fruit topping and chill before serving.

COFFEE & WALNUT CAKE WITH MOCHA ICING

**SERVES: SERVES 6-10 |
TIME: 1 HOUR INCLUDING
BAKING TIME**

This lovely cake isn't difficult to make at all. Just follow the directions and go for it!

(To make a double layer cake, double the cake quantities and use a little of the icing for the centre and the rest on top).

- 1 tbsp flax meal (ground flax seeds) mixed with 3 tbsp hot water and set aside
- 300g/11oz self-raising flour
- 200g/7oz brown sugar
- 60g/2oz walnuts, plus more for decoration
- 1 tsp cinnamon
- 1 tsp baking powder
- 4 tsp instant coffee dissolved in a little boiling water in a jug. Top up with soya or other plant milk to make a total of 300ml/11fl oz
- 170ml/6fl oz oil (use a mild plain vegetable oil)

Mocha icing
- 2½ cups/300g icing sugar, sieved
- ½ cup/50g cocoa powder, sieved (not hot chocolate)
- ¼ cup/60g vegan margarine, eg Pure, Vitalite, Suma
- ¼ cup/60g Trex or similar white vegetable fat (not Flora)
- 3 tsp instant coffee (regular or decaf), dissolved in 2 tbsp hot water
- ½ tsp vanilla essence
- 2-3 tbsp soya, rice or other plant milk

NB All Tate & Lyle sugar is vegan except for Royal Icing.

1 Preheat oven to 180°/350°/Gas Mark 4.
2 Oil a 21cm/8 inch non-stick cake tin (round or square) and line the base with greaseproof paper.
3 Sift the dry ingredients and mix in well, then add nuts and stir well.

4 Pour in wet ingredients and mix well by hand. If the mixture seems very stiff, add 1 tbsp water and mix again.
5 Pour batter into tin and bake for 25-35 minutes. If using a fan-assisted oven, check cake after 25 minutes. Either way, test centre of cake with a cocktail stick or sharp knife – if it comes out clean, the cake is cooked.
6 Allow to cool then carefully remove cake from the tin. Place base side upwards on a wire rack to finish cooling process. Finally, peel off the paper. Turn cake over on to a large plate or the lid of a cake tin before icing it.
7 While the cake is baking, make the icing.
• Electric mixer: place everything in the bowl and whip on high for several minutes until the lumps go and everything is creamy. Chill until needed.
• By hand: cream the fats together with a fork then mix in the icing sugar and cocoa powder until completely smooth and creamy. Add everything else and mix in well. Chill until needed. If the icing is too stiff, add a little cold water. If too thin, add more icing sugar.
8 Use a table or palette knife to put a thin layer of icing on the cake – don't worry if you get a few crumbs in with the icing. Don't mash up the top.
9 Refrigerate for a while then use rest of icing to cover cake. Use a fork or piping bag to make swirls if desired. Decorate with walnut halves and serve. Lovely on its own, or with dairy-free cream or ice-cream.

EAT OUT DAIRY-FREE

Whether you're going for a sandwich or for a sit-down meal, there are plenty of places to find dairy-free options.

Most chains – and increasingly, more independents – carry an allergy list which will contain dairy-free and vegan options. If an independent doesn't offer much, keep asking politely. They want to keep your custom – and it's worth reminding them that parties of mixed customers eat where the dairy-free and vegans can eat. Also, everyone eats dairy-free and vegan food if it's tasty. Keep lobbying the chains too – they tend to be more conservative but they have made changes over the years and will continue to do so if there is customer demand.

VIVA!'S CATERING GUIDE
VEGETARIAN, VEGAN AND DAIRY-FREE CATERING TIPS, £6.99

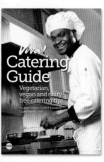

We have a fantastic guide for professional caterers and veggie/vegan customers who want more inclusive menus from restaurants. This stylish, contemporary guide ticks all the boxes. Includes simple definitions of what vegans and veggies eat, ways to 'veganise' classic dishes plus a product and stockists section. All the recipes are suitable for vegans, vegetarians, the lactose and egg intolerant. Buy for your local restaurant to help them get with it. Or download the new updated version FREE!
www.vivashop.org.uk/viva/viva-materials/guides-reports/catering-guide

COFFEE SHOPS
Café Nero, Starbucks and all the major chains now offer soya milk in hot drinks – free or for a small charge. So do many independents, particularly in cities and towns. Soya lattes and soyacinos (the dairy-free alternative to cappuccinos!) are delicious

RESTAURANT CHAINS

Listed below are chains that have at least one dairy-free option, others will have more. If the staff are a bit vague ask to see their free-from/allergens list.

- **ASK ITALIAN**
- **BELLA ITALIA**
- **BOSTON TEA PARTY**
- **CARLUCCIO'S**
- **CHIQUITO**
- **FRANKIE & BENNY'S**
- **GIRAFFE**
- **HANDMADE BURGER COMPANY**
- **JAMIE'S ITALIAN**
- **LAS IGUANAS**
- **LEON**
- **LOUNGERS (EG TINTO LOUNGE)**
- **NANDOS**
- **PIZZA EXPRESS**
- **PIZZA HUT**
- **PRET A MANGER**
- **PREZZO**
- **SUBWAY**
- **TOBY'S CARVERY**
- **WAGAMAMA**
- **WETHERSPOON**
- **ZIZZI**
- **YO SUSHI**

– or ask them to heat some soya milk separately for your Americano/plain coffee! Some chains, eg Little Chef and train caterers are, as yet, sadly lacking – buy your food and hot drinks from station forecourts, eg M&S.

INDEPENDENT RESTAURANTS

Try ethnic food such as Thai (usually a great choice and they use coconut milk instead of dairy milk in cooking); Japanese (again, don't cook with dairy), Chinese (many stir-fried vegetable and bean curd (tofu) dishes will be suitable), Indian (usually a good selection; try a mix of vegetable side dishes with rice; chapattis should be fine. Pakoras, samosas, dhal and poppadoms are usually vegan). Also try veg mezze at Greek and Turkish restaurants.

Pizza is still good without cheese. Pizza Express now offers Pianta Pizza – loaded with spinach, chestnut mushrooms, pine kernels and artichokes on a spicy Arrabbiata base. Domino offers a dairy-free base so get them to pile on extra tomato sauce, garlic and lots of luvverly veg. Or take in your own, unopened packet of vegan cheeze and ask them to use it (and knock a bit off the bill!) Better still, find a pizzeria that offers vegan cheeze – they are springing up around the UK.

MORE EATING OUT INFORMATION

MY VEGAN TOWN www.myvegantown.org.uk – Viva!'s new go-to, global source for everything vegan: eating out, events, accommodation, vegan businesses, vegan groups… and more! You can also add your own listings easily as well as reviews – it's easy.

SUPERMARKET READY-TO-GO MEALS

Chill and salad counters are often a good source of ready to go food, eg multi salads, antipasto etc. Eg M&S, Waitrose, Asda etc. M&S and Waitrose branches in motorway services are also really handy!

VEGANUARY www.veganuary.com/eating-out
HAPPY COW www.happycow.net
TRIP ADVISOR www.tripadvisor.co.uk
VEGETARIAN VISITOR
www.vegetarianvisitor.co.uk
YELP www.yelp.co.uk

There are also several excellent regional websites, eg
■ **EAT OUT VEGAN WALES**
  www.eatoutveganwales.org
■ **VEGAN CORNWALL**
  http://vegancornwall.wordpress.com/bude
■ **VEGETARIAN SCOTLAND**
  www.vegsoc.org/scotlandgroups

And travel guides see
www.vivashop.org.uk/catalog/book-club/travel-guides